Book 3

MY FUN-TO-READ BOOKS

Stories for enjoyment and enrichment

Text adapted by James Ertel

THE SOUTHWESTERN COMPANY • Nashville

The Story of
PABLO
MEXICAN BOY

Illustrations by Arnold Zweerts

THE SOUTHWESTERN COMPANY • Nashville

The True-to-Life photographs in this book are from the educational motion picture, "Mexican Boy—The Story of Pablo," produced by Encyclopaedia Britannica Films, Inc., and directed by William Deneen. In his search for authentic locales and people for educational motion pictures, William Deneen has traveled around the world many times. "Mexican Boy" was photographed in the tiny village of Tepoztlán (1960 population 3,900), located in the Sierra Madres mountains southeast of Mexico City. The principal "actors" in this movie are all members of one family living in Tepoztlán.

The design of this book is by the noted husband-wife team of artists, Alex and Janet D'Amato.

MEXICO CITY

TEPOZTLÁN

This is the village in Mexico where
Pablo lives. There are high mountains
around the village.

Some of the buildings in the village
are hundreds of years old, for Mexico is
an old country. The towers of the old
church can be seen from far away.

Pablo wakes up early every morning.
He sleeps on a straw mat on the floor in
one corner of the house.

Pablo's house has only one room.
Pablo helped his Papa build this house with
mud bricks dried in the sun.

One morning Pablo awoke and shook his piggy bank. He hoped that today he would earn enough more for a pair of real shoes.

Never had he worn real shoes. He always wore sandals. They were strong, but they were not beautiful like real shoes.

In a corner of the room Mama was making corn cakes for breakfast. She cooked them on a low stove.

Pablo saw Papa's two hats hanging on the wall. His hat for everyday was there. So was his other hat for special days. Pablo grinned. It was the most beautiful hat in the world.

Pablo looked at Mama and saw
she was sad. His sister Crispina had been
sick for many days.

Pablo hoped that Crispina would get
well before the feast day at the church.
She must see Papa wear his beautiful hat.
She must see Pablo wear his shiny
black shoes.

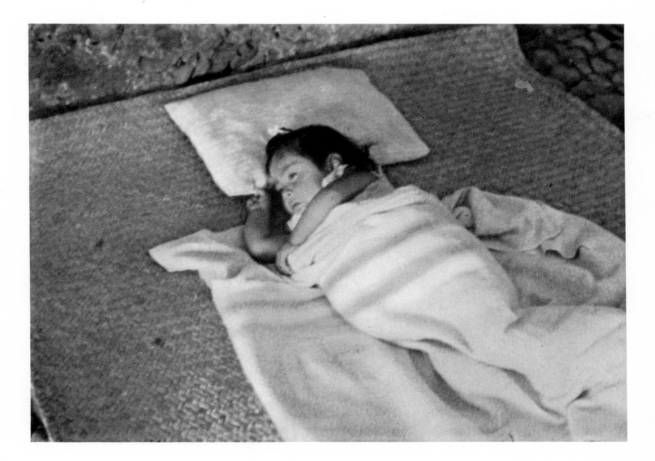

The family sat down to breakfast. Papa and Pablo said it was very good. So did big brother Carlos, and Lolita, the baby.

Pablo was going to help his father that day. He felt like a man.

He put on Papa's beautiful hat to see how it fit him. Everyone laughed at Pablo, but he did not mind.

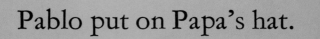

Pablo put on Papa's hat.

After breakfast Papa and Pablo
went out to work. Papa walked in
front, leading their donkey. They had
a long way to go.

Pablo walked behind, thinking of
Crispina. He was hoping she would
get well.

Soon they got to the shady woods
where the coffee beans grow.

They filled many bags with coffee
beans. They loaded the bags on the
donkey and started back home.

When they got the coffee beans
home, Papa and Pablo spread them out
so the hot sun could dry them. After the
beans were dried, they would be sold.

Next it was time to take care of
the cows.

Papa and Carlos and Pablo led the
cows to a hill where there was grass.

While Pablo worked with Carlos and Papa, Mama stayed home.

On some days she went to the market and sold vegetables from her garden, or clay pots and dishes she had made.

But today Mama stayed home because Crispina was sick. She sat in the sun and sewed and thought about Crispina.

Early the next day Pablo was in his
little garden. Some of his tomatoes were
ripe. Pablo picked them and put them
in his hat.

Pablo was happy because Papa let
him take his tomatoes to sell. He
was happy because the market was fun.
And at the market he would see the
beautiful shoes!

Pablo found a place to show his tomatoes in the market. He shouted out how fine his tomatoes were.

A lady with a basket came by. She looked at Pablo's tomatoes. Then she paid Pablo and put all of the tomatoes in her basket.

Now Pablo had almost enough money to buy the beautiful shoes.

Pablo walked through the market. There were fruits and vegetables of all kinds. There were clothes. There were clay pots like the ones his mother used for cooking.

Pablo walked all through the market.

At last he came to the shoe counter. There they were! They would wait for him, those black shoes.

Pablo felt the money in his pocket, "Soon," he said to himself. "Soon I will have enough money to buy those shoes."

On his way home Pablo passed by
the church. Some people from far away
were looking at it. They were taking
pictures of the great door.

Pablo went to one of the men and asked if he might wash the man's car.

It was a very beautiful car. Pablo washed it until it shone like black shoes.

"You have done a fine job," the man said to Pablo.

The man put money into Pablo's hand. Pablo could hardly believe his eyes! Now he had enough money for the shoes!

He ran to tell Mama the good news.

But he stopped when he got near his house.

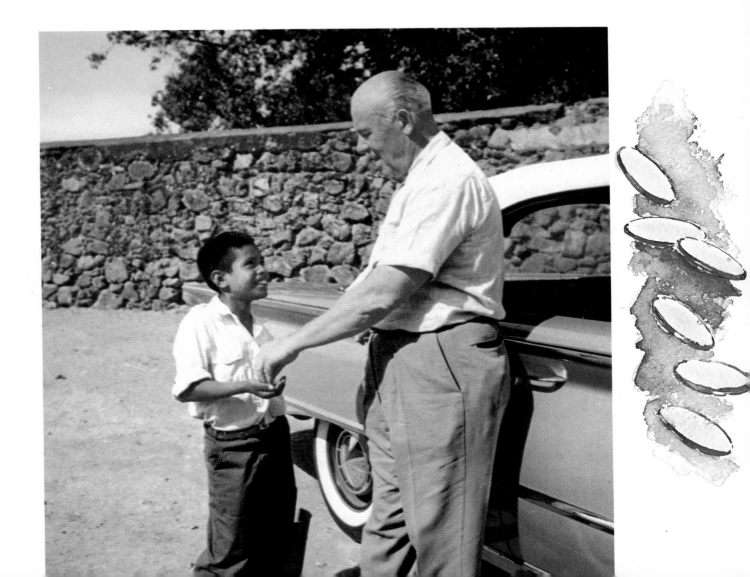

The doctor was talking to Mama.
Crispina needed a medicine which
cost much money.

Pablo said to Mama, "I have the
money."

The great feast day came at last. Pablo and his family had a special breakfast.

Crispina ate with them. She was well again and Pablo was glad. He did not think about the shoes.

The people of the village were
gathering to walk to the church. Everyone was smiling. It was a happy day.

Suddenly Pablo frowned. Papa was
wearing his old hat. Pablo asked,
"Where is your beautiful hat, Papa?"

Papa only looked at him. He did
not answer.

Pablo walked with Papa.

The people started
walking to the church.

After a time they got
near the church. Here Pablo
was going to put on
his new shoes so he could
wear them into the church.
He blinked his eyes and
walked on. He must not
think about that.

Now they were near
the gates of the church. It
seemed that all the people
of the world were at the
church.

Papa took Pablo's arm.
Then a surprising thing
happened.

The gates of the church.

From a bag, Papa brought out the shiny shoes.

Pablo knew now why Papa had not worn his beautiful hat. Papa had sold the hat to get money to buy the shoes.

Pablo and Papa looked at each other. Papa's eyes told how proud he was of his son. To Pablo, that look meant more than anything—even more than new shoes.

ESKIMO FAMILY

Illustrations by Robert Glaubke

THE SOUTHWESTERN COMPANY • Nashville

The true-to-life photographs in this book are from the educational motion picture "Eskimo Family," photographed and produced for Encyclopaedia Britannica Films, Inc., by William Deneen. The film was shot on Baffin Island, near the Arctic Circle.

The design of this book is by Alex D'Amato. Supervision of color reproduction is by James Lockhart.

Baffin Island

Frobisher Bay

ARCTIC CIRCLE

CANADA

HUDSON BAY

Anakudluk and his family live on
Baffin Island near the Arctic Circle.
        Snow and ice cover the land and
sea for nine months of the year.
        In December the sun does not rise
at all. Then Anakudluk and other
Eskimos hunt for food by moonlight.
Many times they find nothing and
then people go to bed hungry.

It was April. This was the time
the Eskimo families traveled south
for the summer. As the days got warmer,
seals would crawl up onto the sea-ice.
Hunting would be good.

Anakudluk harnessed the dogs to the
big sled. The dogs were part wolf, and
were always ready to fight each other.

Mosee, Anakudluk's son, was twelve years old. His father had promised to take him seal hunting this spring.

If Mosee could kill a seal, he would be a young man and not a little boy.

Avinga, Mosee's mother, made all the clothes for the family. She sewed the clothes with tiny stitches so that wind and water could not get through.

Mosee was glad to be leaving the
winter home. The small, round-topped
hut was covered with snow blocks.

Mosee's uncle and his family were
also getting ready to leave.

The sleds of the two families were
piled with tents and poles, clothing, pots,
and food for people and dogs.

Travelling on a dog sled is a
rough ride. There are many jumbled
ice blocks. Hauling a sled over these is
hard work.

When they had traveled about
five miles, the two families stopped
to drink tea.

While the families drank tea, the dogs lay down on the ice. They were too tired to fight.

It was ten degrees below zero, but the dogs did not mind. The air was dry and there was little wind.

Even on the coldest winter nights the dogs slept outside.

Mosee remembered one morning after a heavy snowstorm there was not a dog in sight—just snow mounds. He called the dogs to eat, and the snow seemed to explode.

Each dog could drag a hundred pounds across the ice. It usually took eight or ten dogs to pull a long sled.

At the end of the day Anakudluk
found a good place to camp. Mosee
unhitched the tired dogs and tied
each one to a large rock.

Anakudluk helped Avinga put up the
canvas tent. Avinga had bought the
canvas and made the tent herself.

Avinga and Mosee gathered armfuls
of little willows which grew low over
the ground. Their springy stems
would make a good mattress under the
thick caribou sleeping skins.

The other family camped nearby, and Mosee played a game of ball with his cousin.

When they were smaller, the boys played "dog-team driver." One long pebble was the sled. In front of it were smaller pebbles. These were the dogs.

Little girls built rings of stones and pretended that was a tent. They sat inside the rings with their wooden dolls and played house.

Spear

Fish hook
& Line

After the tent was up,
Anakudluk and Mosee
fished through the sea ice.

Each had a long spear,
and a carved ivory fish
lure. When a fish came near
the lure, they speared it.

The fishing was good.
There was fish for the
family and the dogs.

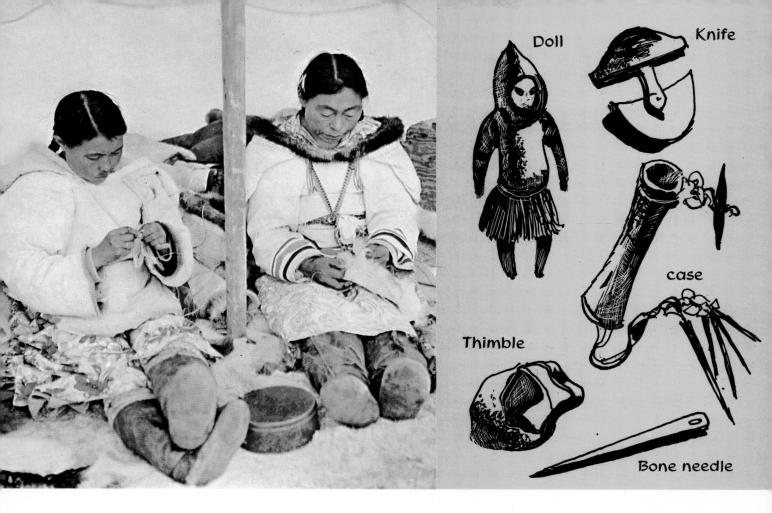

The women sat in Avinga's tent and worked on seal skins. They worked with knives and with bone needles.

Avinga had saved a piece of white skin for a pair of boots for Mosee.

She had cured the skin when the temperature was forty degrees below zero so the cold would turn it white.

The next day was to be Mosee's
first seal hunt.

He knew he had to kill a seal
with the first shot.

Seals always lay close to a crack in
the sea ice. If one were only wounded,
it would roll into the water and swim
under the ice.

Mosee often listened on winter nights to his father and other men talking of hunting seals.

He learned that seals sleep only a few minutes at a time. Then they wake up. If any sound, sight, or smell seems unusual, they dive into the water and swim away.

Mosee and his father put
on their thickest parkas made
of caribou skin.

Mosee and Anakudluk went far out over the ice to where there were patches of sea water.

Suddenly Anakudluk pointed to a seal lying in the sun. Mosee's heart pounded.

Anakudluk had brought white canvas screens. The hunters hid behind these and crept forward.

They went as close as they
dared go.

Mosee raised his rifle. He
took a deep breath, and fired.

Mosee had killed his first seal!

Mosee and Anakudluk took the
seal to the camp.

Avinga met them outside the tent.
She laughed as Anakudluk and Mosee,
talking together, tried to tell her
about the hunt.

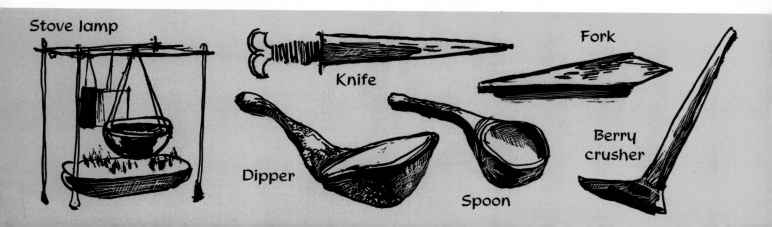

Stove lamp

Knife

Fork

Dipper

Spoon

Berry
crusher

Mosee's father and uncle cut up
the seal. There would be a feast
that night.

None of the seal would be wasted.
Avinga would make boots from the skin.
The fat would burn in the lamp to
heat and light the tent. The bones
would make good soup.

Bowl

Cup

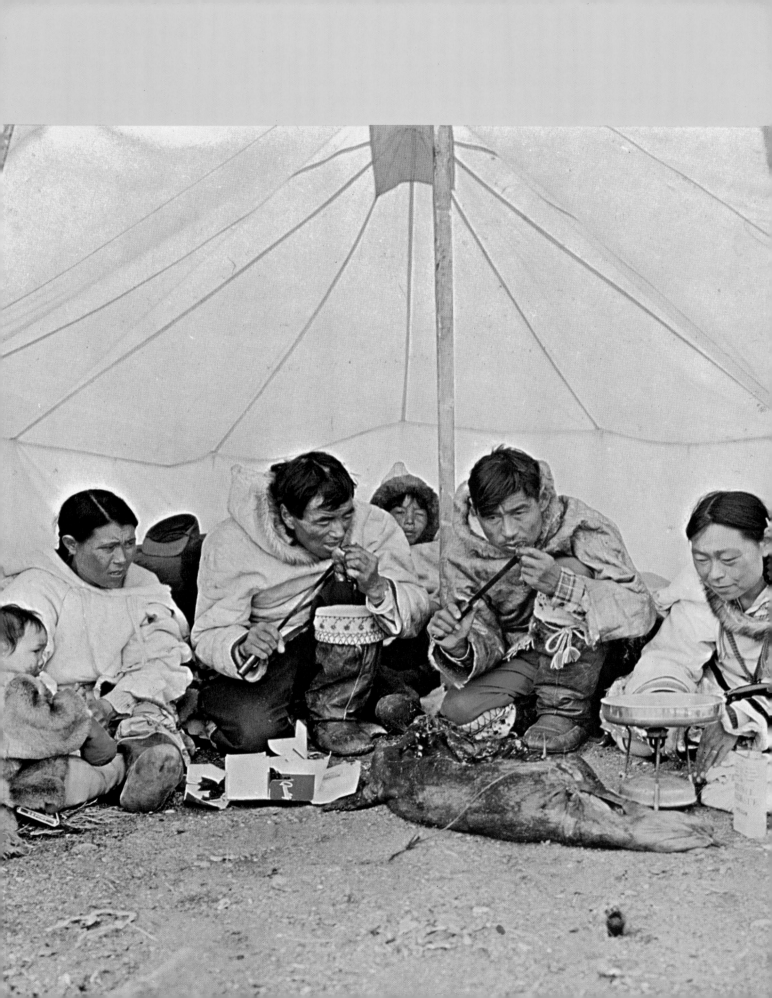

At the feast that night,
everyone ate hungrily. There
was seal meat and bread, which
was cooked on a little stove.

Outside, the dogs smelled
the fresh meat and howled for
their supper. Mosee threw
them pieces of fish.

Anakudluk began to tell stories.
He told about the days before Eskimos
had guns.

Then a hunter could only get
close enough to harpoon a seal by
pretending to be a seal.

He would creep toward a seal. When
the seal raised its head, the hunter
would lie on his side and clap his arms
together like flippers.

In July, the time came to visit
the trading post at Frobisher.

There were wonderful things at
the store—new clothes, shiny pots
and pans, knives and rifles, and
fish hooks.

The baby was put in Avinga's
hood; and the family started out.

At the trading post, Anakudluk
showed his fox skins to the trader.
The fox skins were pure white.
Anakudluk caught
foxes in traps. He covered
the traps with snow.

Anakudluk hoped to save
enough money for a real house
with glass windows.

But it was hard to save enough.
Anakudluk thought how much he
would like a new rifle.

Avinga saw many things she wanted. She wanted some colored thread for trimming parkas and boots. The shiny pots and pans were very beautiful.

Avinga looked around the store. How different things were when her grandmother was a girl!

Then there was no store. The men made all their tools and weapons from bone and wood.

The winter *igloos* were not built of wood, with canvas roofs; they were made of snow blocks. The only heat and light came from blubber lamps.

The sun was still in the sky
when the family got home at midnight.
On summer nights it was hard to sleep
in the bright light.

    But Anakudluk and his family were
tired. They soon fell asleep.

YASIN of Arabia

Illustrations by Arnie Kohn

THE SOUTHWESTERN COMPANY • Nashville

The true-to-life photographs in this book are related to the educational motion picture "Arabian Children," produced by Donald G. Hoffman, and the educational filmstrip "Family of Jordan," both issued by Encyclopaedia Britannica Films, Inc. The photographs were taken by Frank Richter in Jordan.

The design of this book is by Alex D'Amato. Supervision of color reproduction is by James Lockhart.

MEDITERRANEAN SEA

DAMASCUS

CAIRO

ARABIA

KUWAIT

NILE

RED SEA

Yasin lived in a village called
Saahab in the Arabian desert. Only
a few plants grew in the hot, dry
sand of the desert.

Most of the people of Saahab are
farmers. They work hard to try to
make things grow in the desert.

Yasin awoke one morning and heard
the sound of many camel bells. That
meant the bedouins were coming.

Yasin called to his father and
said, "Let us go see the bedouins."
But his father said, "We can see them
from our roof."

Yasin and his brother, Taisir, and
their father climbed to the flat roof.

Yasin's father explained that the
bedouins are fierce desert fighters.
They do not like strangers.

Yasin's sister, Aisha, had gotten
up early. She was helping their
mother cook breakfast.

Before school, the boys had jobs
to do. Taisir had to take the family's
one sheep and one goat to the village
shepherd.

The family kept the sheep for its
wool, and the goat for its milk.

The shepherd was payed to take care
of animals while the farmers worked in
their fields.

Taisir watched the shepherd fill
cans with water. He pulled the water
from a well.

There was nothing for the animals
to eat in the village. The shepherd
had to take the animals a long way
to find grass.

In spring there would be plenty of
grass and the animals would grow fat.

Yasin went with his father to take care of the young fruit trees.

Zenboor, the old camel, knelt down. Yasin's father strapped farm tools on the camel.

Yasin climbed on the camel's back, and they were ready to go.

Father led the camel and Yasin rode. They went through the winding streets of Saahab.

On the way they passed a truck, and Yasin turned to look.

"Can we buy a truck?" he asked his father.

"We cannot even buy a horse," his father said.

Yasin and his father went across desert land. This land was too hard and dry to grow things.

They came to their young fruit trees. Yasin's father had planted them on the side of a hill. There, rain water would reach them as it ran down the hill.

Yasin wanted to look at a young fig tree he had planted. He had covered it with stones to protect it from the sun and sand.

Yasin took away the stones and looked at the young tree.

His father gave him a water can, and Yasin ran to the well.

The well belonging to Yasin's
family was covered with an iron
lid. The lid was kept locked, for
water was scarce in the desert.

Each family owned a well, or
shared one with another family.
Some of the wells were more than a
thousand years old.

Yasin lowered a can into the
well. He carried the can of water
back to his father.

His father poured the water
around the young fig tree.
Yasin watched.

   Now it was nearly time for
school. Yasin covered the fig
tree again.

Yasin ran back across the desert
to the village. He could hear the
school bell ringing. He had to hurry
or he would be late.

He liked school. There he learned
about other parts of the world.
He had never been away from his village,
but he knew about other countries
and about great cities.

Yasin studied the history of his own country in school. He was proud of his country.

He also studied English, arithmetic, science, and agriculture.

He liked to read the books he could get from the school library.

The school building was new.
It was outside the village, where
there was room for a playground.

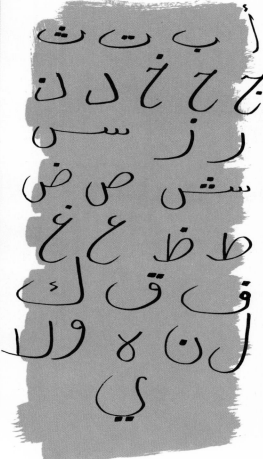

Yasin joined the boys lined up
in the school yard. They went
to their classrooms.

Yasin went to his English class.
He had been confused at first
because English writing goes from
left to right.

His own language, Arabic, goes the
other way. It goes from right to left.

At home Aisha helped her mother.
She did not go to school.

In most Arab villages it was believed
that only boys should go to school.

Aisha got water from the village
well. She poured the water into a jar.

She lifted the jar to the top of her
head. Even though she was young
and small, she carried the jar
easily. She learned to do this
when she was about four years old.

Some of the water Aisha brought
was used by her mother to make bread.
The family ate rice, vegetables
and sometimes meat. But their main
food was bread.

When the bread loaves were ready,
Aisha's mother took them to an oven
to bake.

At meal times the family sat on the floor around a low table. They all ate with their fingers.

When the housework was finished,
Aisha started sewing. She and her
mother made their own clothes.
While Aisha sewed, her mother
made a basket from colored straw.

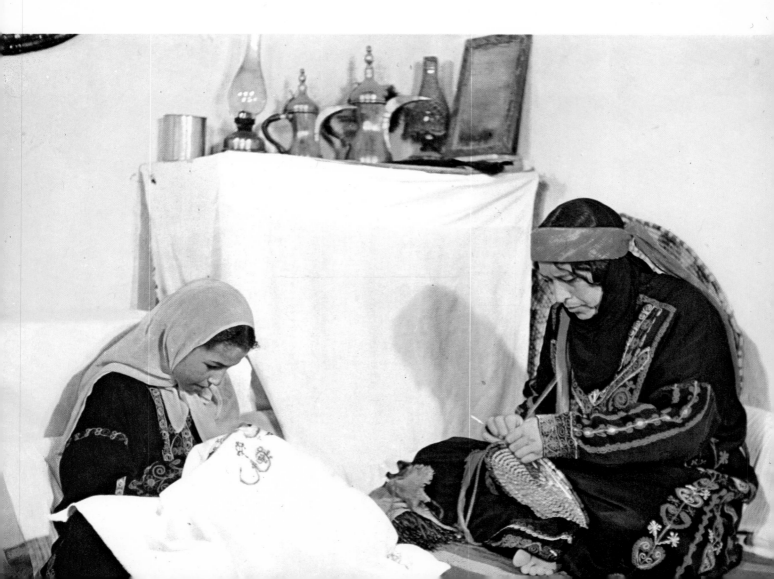

Aisha used colored threads for her sewing. She did not need a pattern book, because she knew the patterns by heart.

These patterns had been handed down from mother to daughter in her family for hundreds of years.

Sometimes Aisha used wool thread which she made herself. She washed the wool and combed it.

She made it into thread.

The wool came from the family sheep.

By noon, Father was hot and
tired. He and old Zenboor had
been working all morning.

Father sat down in the shade of
a big rock. He looked at some
sheep standing in the hot sun.

Father drank water. He ate a
lunch of bread and dates.

He looked at the field he had
been ploughing. He would plant it
with barley.

He had heard that barley would
sell at a good price.

In the afternoon, Yasin and Taisir
met some friends on the way home from
school. They stopped to play a game.

The game was like hopscotch.

Yasin got tired of the game. He
had some money in his pocket. There
was a candy store near by.

He whispered to Taisir. The
two boys ran off.

In the candy store, there were many glass jars full of candy.

Yasin did not often have money for candy. The boys looked at the jars for a long time.

Finally they bought candied fruit.

At the end of the day,
Yasin went to meet his father.
He helped load the farm tools
on the camel's back. He
climbed up behind them.

On their way home, they
had to go near the camp of the
bedouins.

Suddenly two men in the
camp jumped on their horses.
The horses ran fast across
the desert toward Yasin and
his father.

Yasin saw them coming.
He was frightened.